ART RULES

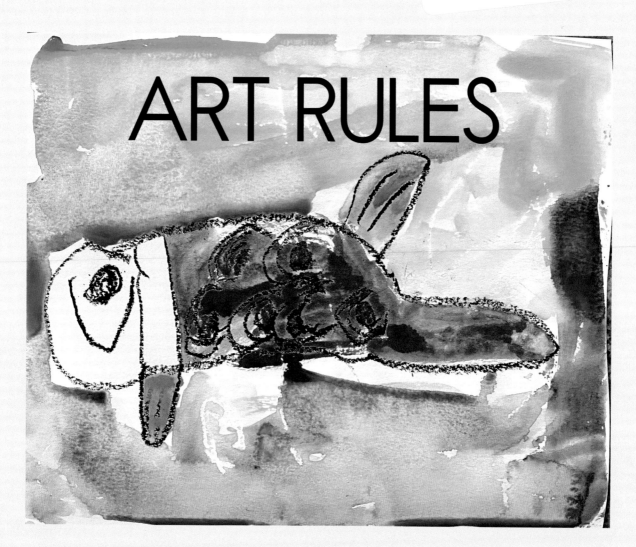

ISBN 978-0-9990120-2-4

ART
RULES

by
Danielle Chammas & Zeina Henry

Little Feet Press

They may tell us that a snowman
Must be three balls tall,
But we won't let them trick us.
That's not true at all!

How many balls to use?
That's up to you and me!
When making art, we decide
What number it should be.

Or maybe instead of balls
We'll stack a bunch of squares.
Or triangles? Or painted rocks?
Or a snowman made of pears?

They may tell us when we're painting
That the sky must be blue,
But that is just too silly.
We know that isn't true.

Skies can be pink or yellow,
Or purple, red, or green.
Skies can be any color
That our creative minds can dream!

When we are making art,
There's more than one right way.
We imagine, and we change.
We experiment and play.

The cool thing about art
Is that we decide the rules:
We can choose any colors,
Any ideas, any tools.

We can create with bottle caps,
Plastic cups, or twine,
Unused buttons, paper scraps,
Anything we can find!

They may give us a frame
As a place to draw our face.
Perhaps instead of inside,
We'll use the outside space?

We might draw two eyes,
Just like a real face.
But when we make art,
This need not be the case.

We can choose three eyes,
Or teeth made out of corn,
An upside down nose,
Or a unicorn horn!

Even when given a paper,
We're not stuck inside the border.
We can tape or glue on fringe
In any direction or order.

Or maybe we will draw
An elephant's long nose
But then go off the page
For its body and its toes.

In the real world,
Rainbows start with red,
But in art, we make the rules.
We can start with blue instead.

They say when using a pencil
To draw with the tip of the lead,
But we can flip it around
To paint with the eraser instead.

They say to use a paintbrush
To spread the paint on papers,
But sometimes we use rocks,
Or leaves, or twigs as scrapers.

Or we squirt out drops of paint
From a ketchup bottle squeezer.
We can spread it with our fingers
Or with ice cubes from the freezer.

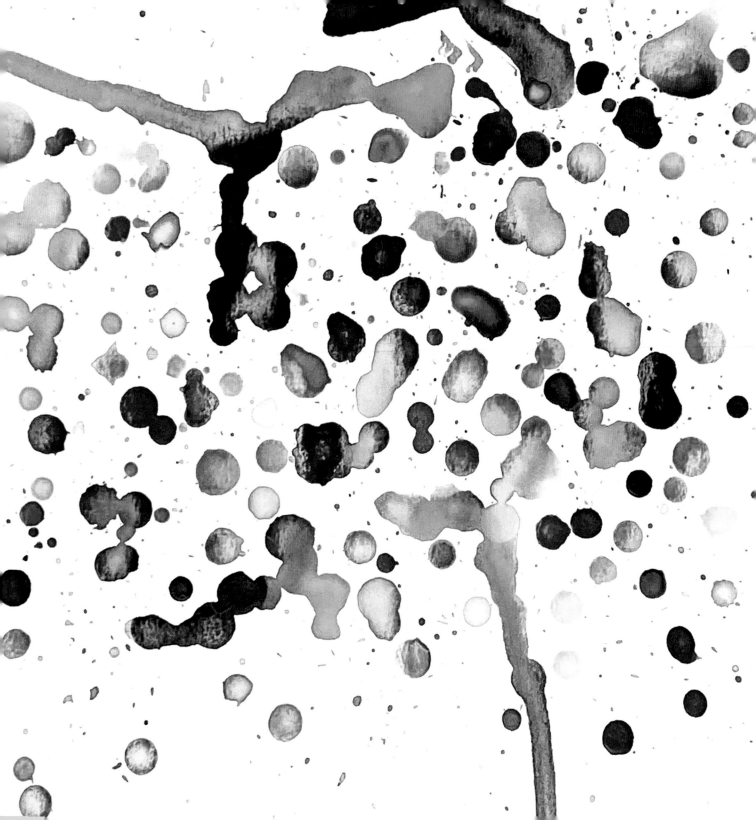

They may tell us not to spill,
And that advice may be quite true...
But if one day we do spill paint,
Here's an experiment we can do:

Take that great big puddle of paint
And stick our paper in it,
Then pull it out to see the print--
With art there is no limit!

With art there is no wrong,
No need to hesitate.
Mistakes are new adventures
That change what we create.

Here's a little secret:
Turtles can be blue.
Water can be purple.
Suns can be red too.

Our very favorite art rule
That we want to share:
What matters more than product
Is HOW we get there.

What matters is the process,
And giving our ideas a try.
Fun experimenting lets
Our imaginations fly!

The End.

About the Creators

Zeina Henry, age 5, has a passion for the creative process and a firm belief that anything is possible in the domain of art. She wanted to create this book for "everybody," as she believes everybody can be an artist.

Her co-creator, Danielle Chammas, is a mother, physician, and author of two other children's books: A Wish From a Fish & An OOPS Sort of Day.

Zoe Henry, age 3, and Sami Henry, age 1, were creative consultants.

Little Feet Press